How I to the World

A Play

by Gary Bedel
illustrated by Len Ebert

 **Harcourt**

Orlando   Boston   Dallas   Chicago   San Diego

Visit *The Learning Site!*
www.harcourtschool.com

Cast

Ish (mother)
Nop (father)
Bo (their son)
Fir (their daughter)
Om (Bo's pet wolf)

SCENE 1

(*The cave of the Urg family.*)

Ish (*wrapping her arms around herself*): It's so cold in here!
Nop (*to Ish*): You know it will be cold until spring. It always is.

Fir: I want some warm food!

Nop: Now, dear, you know there won't be any warm food until spring, either.

Bo: I wish I could make it warm. (*petting Om*) You would like it to be warm, too, wouldn't you? (*Om nods his head.*)

Bo (*to himself*): There must be something we can do. I have an idea! (*Bo runs outside. He returns with lava rocks.*) We can use these rocks to keep warm! The last time the volcano was erupting, the lava made these rocks!

Fir (*walking offstage*): I hate rocks! Besides, they're not warm anymore!

(*Suddenly, Om runs offstage.*)

Bo: Where are you going? Come back, Om! (*to Fir*) See what you did? Now my wolf is gone!

(*Om returns with a stick in his mouth. It is on fire.*)

Bo: Wow! What is that?

Fir: Mom! Dad! The wolf is trying to hurt us! Come quickly!

(*Ish and Nop come rushing in.*)

Ish: What is Om doing? Get him out of here! (*She runs after Om, who escapes out of the cave.*)

Nop (*to Bo*): I knew that wolf would be trouble! I don't ever want to see it in here again!

Bo: Please, Dad! Om would never try to hurt us!

Nop: Son, it's just too dangerous. (*sneezes*) Besides, I'm allergic to him.

Bo: I have to find him! (*He runs out to find Om.*)

Ish: All right, don't bring back that dangerous wolf!

SCENE 2

(*Bo and Om are sitting together outside the cave.*)

Bo (*petting Om*): I know you would never hurt us, but Dad was really angry.
(*Om gets up and barks at something offstage.*)
Bo: What are you saying, boy?
(*Om barks again. He puts his paw on Bo and looks offstage.*)

Bo: What are you saying? Over there is the erupting volcano. (*Om nods strongly.*)

Bo: What? It's red. It's hot. Is that it? It's hot? Om, it's too far away. I tried using lava rocks to stay warm, but they aren't hot now.

(*Om brings Bo another burning stick. Bo holds his hand near it.*)

Bo: Can we use this to keep warm? (*Om nods his head.*)

Bo (*looking at the stick*): I don't understand, Om.

(*Om brings more sticks. The fire gets very big.*)

Bo (*His eyes open wide.*): I'm getting hot, Om! This is how we can stay warm! (*He hugs Om. Then Om runs offstage and comes back with an egg.*)

Bo: Now what? (*Om drops the egg on a hot rock. The egg cooks.*) Oh! Warm food! (*He tastes the cooked egg.*) This is delicious! (*Om wags his tail.*)
Bo (*thinking*): Now, the hard part will be getting everyone else to understand.

SCENE 3

(Ish, Nop, and Fir sit shivering inside the cave.)

Bo: Mom? Dad? Can I show you something?

Ish: Does it have to do with Om?

Bo: Well, yes—

Nop: Then no! We are trying to have a peaceful day!

(Outside the cave, Bo stands thinking. Then he snaps his fingers.)

Bo: I know! *(He gathers sticks.)* Go get the fire, Om!

(Om brings a burning branch.)

Bo: Put the branch on these twigs. *(The twigs catch fire.)* Now, go get some eggs! *(Om brings eggs.)*

Bo: Good boy! *(Bo cooks the eggs and folds them over gently.)*

Ish: What's that smell? (*The family comes out of the cave.*)

Fir: That smells wonderful! What is it?

Bo: I call this dish an omelet, after Om. We will be warm, Mom, and eat warm food, Fir! Om showed me how to do it. We will never have to be cold again!

Nop (*getting close to the fire*): Wow, that's warm. (*He tastes the eggs.*) Hmm, your omelet would make a fine brunch dish. This wolf taught you that?

Bo: Yes, sir. All of it.

Nop (*looking at Om*): I'm sorry we asked you to leave, Om. You have changed our lives. We will share your gift with everyone we meet. Thanks to you, no one will be cold again.